SUMMER OF THE MONKEYS

by
Wilson Rawls

Student Packet

Written by
Monica L. Odle

Contains masters for:

2	Prereading Activities
6	Vocabulary Activities
1	Study Guide
2	Comprehension Activities
3	Character Analysis Activities
5	Literary Analysis Activities
2	Critical Thinking Activities
1	Writing Activity
3	Quizzes
1	Novel Test

PLUS   Detailed Answer Key
and Scoring Rubric

Teacher Note

Selected activities, quizzes, and test questions in this Novel Units® Student Packet are labeled with the appropriate reading/language arts skills for quick reference. These skills can be found above quiz/test questions or sections and in the activity headings.

Note

The 2001 Dell Laurel-Leaf paperback edition of the novel, © 1976 by Woodrow Wilson Rawls, was used to prepare this guide. Page references may differ in other editions. Novel ISBN: 978-0-553-29818-5

Please note: Please assess the appropriateness of this novel for the age level and maturity of your students prior to reading and discussing it with them.

ISBN 978-1-60878-528-5

To order, contact your local school supply store, or—

Novel Units, Inc.
P.O. Box 97
Bulverde, TX 78163-0097

Web site: novelunits.com

Note to the Teacher

Selected activities, quizzes, and test questions in this Novel Units® Student Packet are labeled with the following reading/language arts skills for quick reference. These skills can be found above quiz/test questions or sections and in the activity headings.

Basic Understanding: The student will demonstrate a basic understanding of written texts. The student will:
- use a text's structure or other sources to locate and recall information (Locate Information)
- determine main idea and identify relevant facts and details (Main Idea and Details)
- use prior knowledge and experience to comprehend and bring meaning to a text (Prior Knowledge)
- summarize major ideas in a text (Summarize Major Ideas)

Literary Elements: The student will apply knowledge of literary elements to understand written texts. The student will:
- analyze characters from a story (Character Analysis)
- analyze conflict and problem resolution (Conflict/Resolution)
- recognize and interpret literary devices (flashback, foreshadowing, symbolism, simile, metaphor, etc.) (Literary Devices)
- consider characters' points of view (Point of View)
- recognize and analyze a story's setting (Setting)
- understand and explain themes in a text (Theme)

Analyze Written Texts: The student will use a variety of strategies to analyze written texts. The student will:
- identify the author's purpose (Author's Purpose)
- identify cause and effect relationships in a text (Cause/Effect)
- identify characteristics representative of a given genre (Genre)
- interpret information given in a text (Interpret Text)
- make and verify predictions with information from a text (Predictions)
- sequence events in chronological order (Sequencing)
- identify and use multiple text formats (Text Format)
- follow written directions and write directions for others to follow (Follow/Write Directions)

Critical Thinking: The student will apply critical-thinking skills to analyze written texts. The student will:
- write and complete analogies (Analogies)
- find similarities and differences throughout a text (Compare/Contrast)
- draw conclusions from information given (Drawing Conclusions)
- make and explain inferences (Inferences)
- respond to texts by making connections and observations (Making Connections)
- recognize and identify the mood of a text (Mood)
- recognize an author's style and how it affects a text (Style)
- support responses by referring to relevant aspects of a text (Support Responses)
- recognize and identify the author's tone (Tone)
- write to entertain, such as through humorous poetry or short stories (Write to Entertain)
- write to express ideas (Write to Express)
- write to inform (Write to Inform)
- write to persuade (Write to Persuade)
- demonstrate understanding by creating visual images based on text descriptions (Visualizing)
- practice math skills as they relate to a text (Math Skills)

Name _____

Anticipation and Reaction

Directions: Consider the following statements before you read the novel. Place a checkmark in one of the boxes to show whether you agree or disagree with each statement, and provide your reasoning. After you have completed the novel, mark your responses again. Provide an explanation for why your opinion changed or remained the same.

Statement	Response Before Reading	Response After Reading
1. Generosity should be rewarded.	☐ you agree with the statement ☐ you disagree with the statement	☐ you agree with the statement ☐ you disagree with the statement
2. Animals can sense people's emotions.	☐ you agree with the statement ☐ you disagree with the statement	☐ you agree with the statement ☐ you disagree with the statement
3. People must help their wishes become reality.	☐ you agree with the statement ☐ you disagree with the statement	☐ you agree with the statement ☐ you disagree with the statement
4. With hard work, a person can accomplish anything.	☐ you agree with the statement ☐ you disagree with the statement	☐ you agree with the statement ☐ you disagree with the statement

Name _____

The Title Tells All

Directions: Use the chart below to make predictions about the novel.

Title of Novel:
Based on the title, what do you think the novel will be about?
In the space provided below, create an illustration for the novel based on the title.
After reading the first chapter, write a paragraph predicting what will happen in the rest of the novel.

Name _____

Vocabulary Fill-in

sharecropper	contraption	grove	altar
slough	jarred	scalded	liable
lobe	peddler	radiant	

Directions: Fill in the blanks below using the vocabulary words from the list above. Then, define the two vocabulary words you did NOT use.

The old (1) _____ was tired of working other people's fields. He loved the land

he worked, especially the scenery of the huge apple (2) _____ nearby. He also

appreciated having access to every farming (3) _____ imaginable. All in all, his

work was satisfying, but the ground he cultivated wasn't his own. He observed the hogs, perfectly

content in their (4) _____. He suddenly realized that while he could dream

of his future, he had to find a way to be content with the present. He knew he was

(5) _____ to get cranky if he didn't find a bright spot in his work today.

He pulled distractedly on the (6) _____ of his ear as he surveyed the farm.

The land appeared warm, golden, and (7) _____. He nodded to a

(8) _____ ambling down the road selling his wares. Yes, today was a good

day. He was (9) _____ suddenly from his thoughts by the sounds of the farm

around him. He took a deep breath, smiled, and returned to his work.

10. Word: _____

Definition: _____

_____

11. Word: _____

Definition: _____

_____

Vocabulary Chart

kindling	quavering	spindly	squalling
briers	timber	superstitious	loping
hallowed	darted		

Directions: Place each vocabulary word in the correct column in the chart according to how it is used in the novel.

Noun	Verb	Adjective	Adverb

Name _____

Vocabulary Matching

aggravate	stale	flouncing	underbrush
salve	still	commotion	milling
lapping			

A. Directions: Match each word to the BEST definition.

_____ 1. aggravate   a. scene of noisy confusion or activity

_____ 2. stale   b. bushes or small trees growing in a wooded area

_____ 3. flouncing   c. drinking something with the tongue

_____ 4. underbrush   d. soothing, healing ointment

_____ 5. salve   e. to anger, irritate, or annoy someone

_____ 6. still   f. tool for distilling liquids

_____ 7. commotion   g. moving with exaggerated or lively motions

_____ 8. milling   h. moving about restlessly

_____ 9. lapping   i. still, stagnant

B. Directions: Using at least three words from the vocabulary list above, write a short summary of Chapters 7–9.

_____

_____

_____

_____

_____

_____

_____

_____

Word Map

blot	unruly	portion	trough
flares	buckboard	quiver	twine
deliberately			

Directions: Complete a word map like the one below for five of the vocabulary words above.

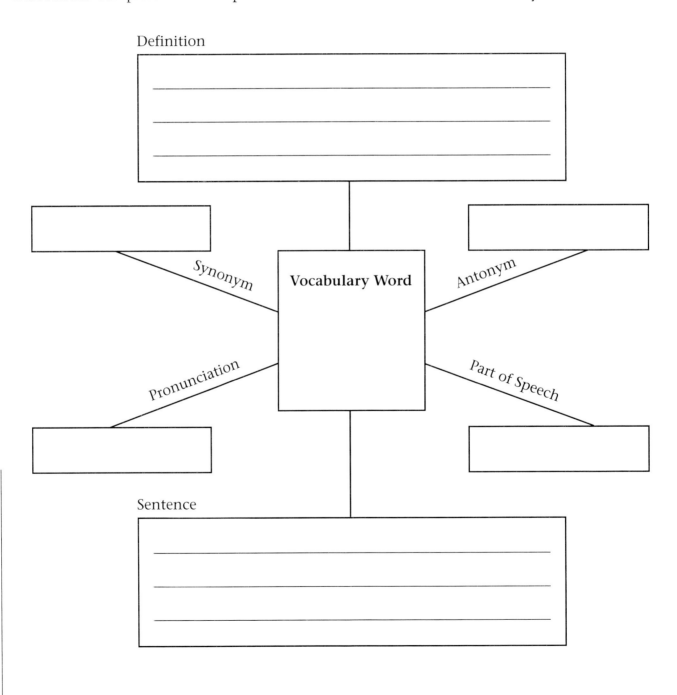

Name _____

Vocabulary Mobile

chariot	liniment	pneumonia	forge
legend	dowry	mercy	drift
boring	utter	pitiful	

Directions: Working in groups of five, choose at least five words from the vocabulary list above and make a triangle for each. Cut a nine-inch square out of white construction paper. Fold the paper in half diagonally (from corner to corner). Unfold the paper. Fold the paper in half again (Figure A). Then, cut one line from the outer corner to the center of the paper (Figure B). Slide one cut piece on top of the other to form a triangular shape resembling a pyramid, but without a base. (Figure C). Glue the pieces together. On one side, write a vocabulary word, its definition, a synonym, and an antonym (if applicable). On another side, write a sentence using the vocabulary word. On the third side, draw a picture to illustrate the vocabulary word. All groups should combine their triangles and hang them in the classroom as a mobile.

Figure A

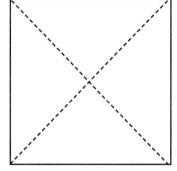

1–Fold in half diagonally

2–Fold in half again

Figure B

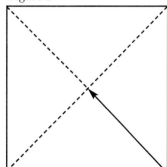

Cut from corner to center in direction of arrow

Figure C

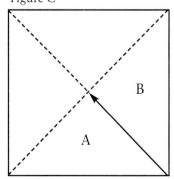

Slide one cut piece (A) on top of the other cut piece (B)

Vocabulary Crossword

cinch	roan	tendon	wiry
mocked	unbearable	moping	primitive

Directions: Complete the crossword puzzle below using the clues given.

Across
3. imitated; mimicked
5. brown, black, or reddish-brown coat speckled with white or gray
6. certainty; sure bet
7. slim but muscular
8. tough band connecting muscle to bone

Down
1. difficult, unpleasant, or impossible
2. wandering around sadly
4. undeveloped; unsettled

Name _____

Directions: Respond to the following items on a separate sheet of paper. Use your answers in class discussions, for writing assignments, and to review for tests.

Chapters 1–3

1. Where is the Lee family's farm located?
2. How did Jay Berry's and Daisy's births differ?
3. How did Jay Berry's parents get 60 acres of land?
4. Why did Mama insist on spending the family's first night in the Oklahoma Territory on the farm land?
5. Describe how Daisy decorated her playhouse.
6. Why does Jay Berry take Rowdy with him to the river bottoms?
7. What is Papa's explanation for a monkey's presence in the river bottoms?
8. How does Jay Berry's grandfather explain the monkey's presence in the river bottoms?
9. How does Jay Berry's grandfather make monkey traps?
10. What does Jay Berry remind his mother that he's always wanted?
11. Why does Daisy initially object to Jay Berry's monkey hunting?
12. Who does Daisy believe can curse a person with bad luck?

Chapters 4–6

1. Why does Papa worry about Jay Berry's first monkey-catching attempt?
2. Why doesn't Jay Berry allow Rowdy to chase any animals in the river bottoms?
3. What does Jay Berry mistake the hundred dollar monkey for when he first sees him?
4. How does the hundred dollar monkey avoid the traps (but take the bait) the first and second times Jay Berry sets them?
5. What happens to Jay Berry's belongings when he and Rowdy leave to drink from the spring?
6. How does Jay Berry anger the hundred dollar monkey?
7. Why can't Jay Berry try to catch only the small monkeys, as Papa advises?
8. Why does Mama worry immediately when she sees Jay Berry?
9. What device does Jay Berry's grandfather give him to help him catch the monkeys?
10. Describe Jay Berry's grandmother.
11. Why are Jay Berry's parents and grandparents steadily saving money?
12. With whom does Jay Berry "get even" using the net his grandfather lent him?
13. Who helps Jay Berry dig a hole for a new monkey trap?

Chapters 7–9

1. What two creatures enter the hole and bother Jay Berry and Rowdy?
2. Why do the two monkeys Jay Berry catches bite him and Rowdy?
3. What does Jay Berry think the hundred dollar monkey is trying to communicate to him?
4. Why do Jay Berry and Rowdy eventually leave the river bottoms without the monkeys they had caught?
5. What disease does Daisy suspect Jay Berry and Rowdy may have contracted?
6. How does Daisy get Rowdy into the same room with Jay Berry so she can "watch both of them" (p. 118)?
7. For how long is Jay Berry sick?
8. What is the big monkey's name, and how does Jay Berry's grandfather know it?
9. What new idea does Jay Berry's grandfather have for catching the monkeys?
10. Where does Jay Berry find the monkeys?
11. Why does Jimbo react the way he does when Jay Berry refuses the can of sour mash?
12. What is Jay Berry missing when he awakens?
13. Why is Mama upset with Jay Berry when he returns home?

Chapters 10–12

1. What does Papa tell Jay Berry about sour mash?
2. Why is Jay Berry surprised that Daisy stayed home to take care of him?
3. Why does Daisy "prescribe" a dose of castor oil for Jay Berry?
4. Why does Jay Berry's grandfather suggest visiting the library in town?
5. What opportunity does Jay Berry's grandfather offer him on the way to town?
6. What does the Carnegie Library look like?
7. What book does the librarian bring Jay Berry and his grandfather?
8. Why do Jay Berry and his grandfather stop at Wiley Mercantile?
9. What does Jay Berry buy at the store for each member of his family?
10. What is Jay Berry's grandfather's newest plan for monkey trapping?
11. How do Jay Berry and his grandfather lose what they bought at Wiley Mercantile?
12. How does Jay Berry ease Daisy's anger at him?

Chapters 13–15

1. What is Jay Berry afraid might happen during the storm?
2. What does Jay Berry discover about Daisy's leg during the storm?
3. What does Daisy claim the Old Man of the Mountains was doing during the storm?
4. What does Papa invite Jay Berry to help with the next morning?
5. What miraculous discovery does Daisy make?
6. What couple does Mama describe in her story?
7. What wish does Jay Berry make?
8. How does Jay Berry locate the monkeys in the washout?
9. How is Jay Berry's interaction with the monkeys different this time than all of the other times? Why?
10. How does Jay Berry revive the monkeys?
11. Why does Papa agree with Jay Berry that the monkeys wanted to be caught?
12. What does each family member offer to do for the monkeys?

Chapters 16–19

1. How do Jay Berry and his grandfather plan to get a message to the circus owners?
2. What "wish" comes true for Rowdy?
3. Why does Jay Berry's grandfather go to Indian Tom's?
4. How does Jimbo react to seeing Ben Johnson?
5. How much money does Jay Berry receive as a reward?
6. Why is Jay Berry drawn to the paint pony but hesitant to choose her?
7. Why does Jay Berry describe the walk back to his grandfather's store as "the longest walk [he] had ever taken in [his] life" (p. 266)?
8. How do Jay Berry's family members react when he gives Mama the sack filled with money?
9. How do Papa and Jay Berry fare while Mama and Daisy are gone?
10. Why is Jay Berry amazed when he sees Daisy at the train depot?
11. What surprise is waiting for Jay Berry at the Lees' home when the family returns?
12. What does Daisy ask Jay Berry to do?

Name _____

Time Line

Directions: In the numbered boxes, write four main events that occur during Jay Berry's monkey-trapping adventures. Write them in the order they occur in the story. In the larger boxes, describe the event or draw a picture representing the event.

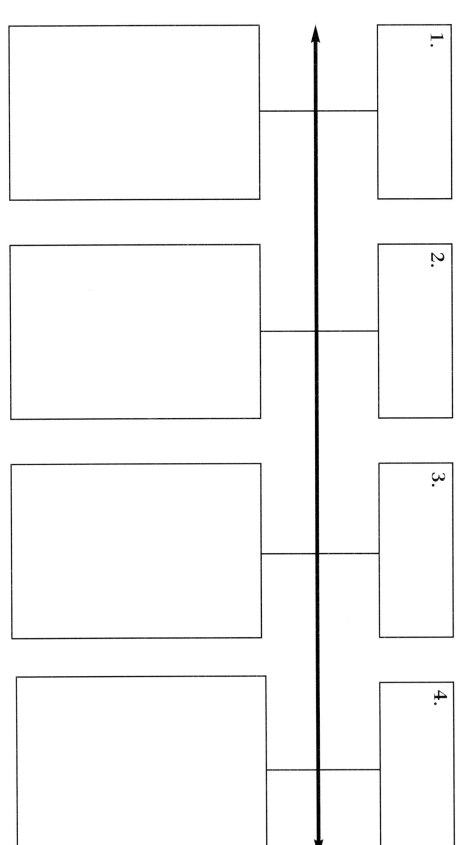

Name _____

Character Analysis Blocks

Directions: Select a character from the novel to describe using the blocks below.

Who is the character?

What does the character do?	Why does s/he do it?

What, if anything, is significant about the character's name?	What is the nature of this character's actions? *(reactive, active, important, consequential, secondary)*	What is the significance of the novel's time and place to the character?

What is unusual or important about the character?	How does the character change in the story?	Does the character remind you of another character from another novel? Who?	Do you know anyone similar to this character?

Name _____

Conflict

The **conflict** of a story is the struggle between two people or two forces. There are three main types of conflict: person vs. person, person vs. nature or society, and person vs. self.

Directions: The characters experience some conflicts in the story. In the chart below, list the names of three major characters. In the space provided, list a conflict each character experiences. Then, explain how each conflict is resolved in the story.

Character:

Conflict	Resolution

Character:

Conflict	Resolution

Character:

Conflict	Resolution

Name _____

Sociogram

Directions: On the "spokes" surrounding each character's name, write several adjectives that describe that character. How does one character influence another? On the arrows joining one character to another, write a description of the relationship between the two characters. Remember, relationships go both ways, so each line requires a descriptive word.

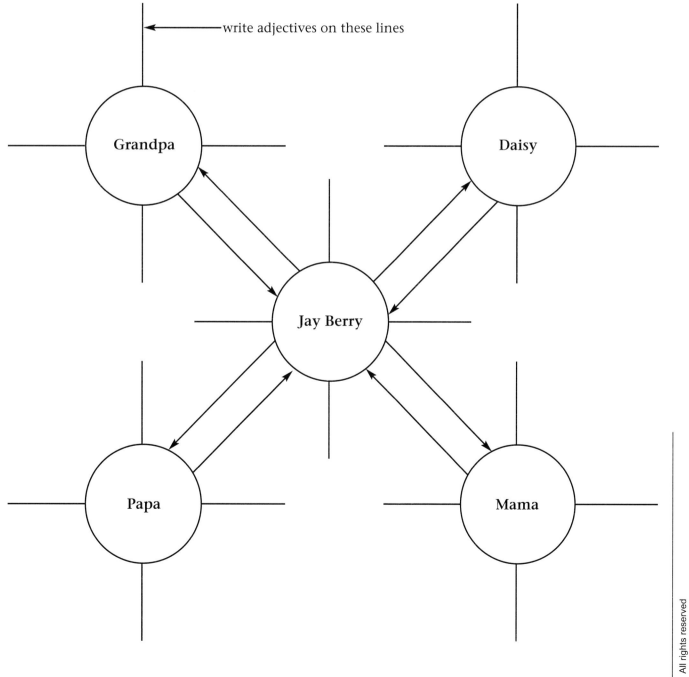

Cause/Effect Chart

Directions: In the empty boxes, describe several effects that result from Jay Berry catching the monkeys.

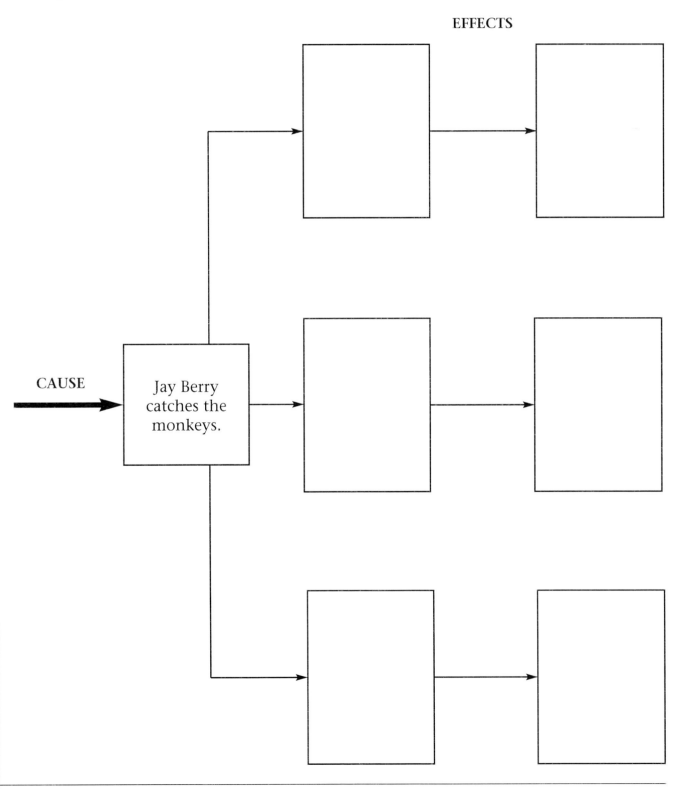

Name _____

A Character's World

Directions: You may be able to draw parallels between a character's world and your own. Write a character's name in the blank. Describe that character's world. Then describe a related situation or event from your own world.

_____'s World

_____

_____

_____

My World

_____

_____

_____

_____'s World

_____

_____

_____

My World

_____

_____

_____

_____'s World

_____

_____

_____

My World

_____

_____

_____'s World

_____

_____

_____

My World

_____

_____

Name _____

Solving Problems

Directions: List six problems the characters in the novel face. Then complete the rest of the chart. For each problem, circle which solution you think is best—yours or the character's.

Problem	Character's Solution	Your Solution

Name _____

Rainstorming

Directions: In the clouds below, describe some effects of the storm that hits the Lees' farm and the river bottoms.

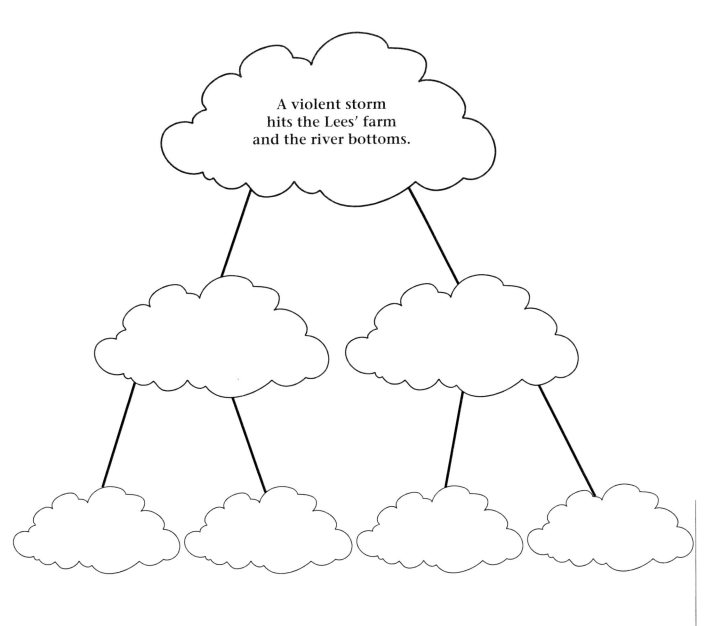

A violent storm
hits the Lees' farm
and the river bottoms.

Name _____

Who Am I?

Directions: Write a riddle describing a character in the novel. Include adjectives, adverbs, nouns, and verbs that will help other students see this character in their mind's eye. Describe how the person looks, acts, feels, talks, and how other people in the story treat this character. (Do not reveal which character is the answer to your riddle.)

Who am I?

I have

_____

_____

_____

_____

I can

_____

_____

_____

In the story, people say I

_____

_____

_____

Who am I? _____

© Novel Units, Inc.

Name _____

Story Map

Directions: Complete the story map below.

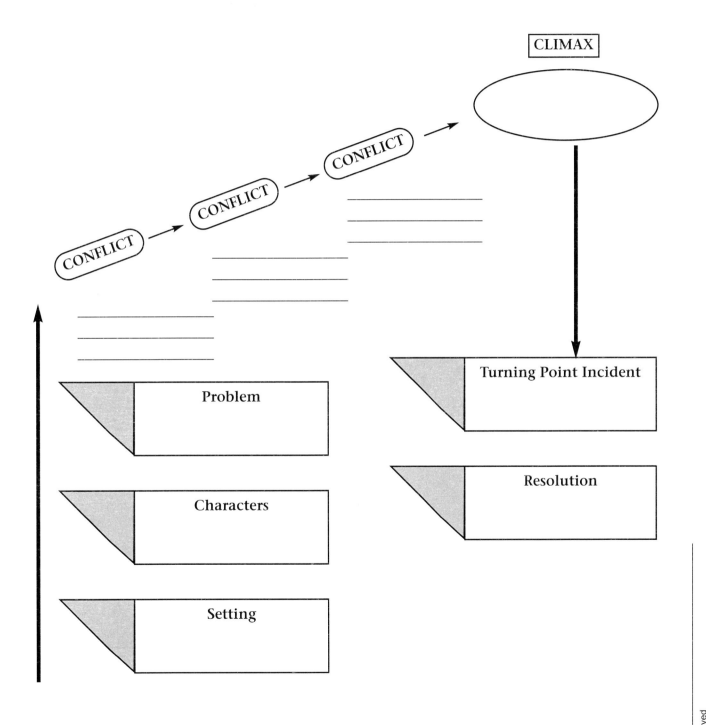

Name _____

Effects of Reading

Directions: Think about how parts of the novel affected you in different ways. Did some parts make you laugh? cry? want to do something to help someone? Below, list one part of the novel that touched each of the following parts of the body: your head (made you think), your heart (made you feel), your funny bone (made you laugh), or your feet (spurred you to action).

Your head	Your heart

Your funny bone	Your feet

Name _____

Thematic Analysis

Directions: Choose a theme from the novel to be the focus of your word web. On the spokes, provide examples from the novel that support the theme. Then, answer the question in each starred box.

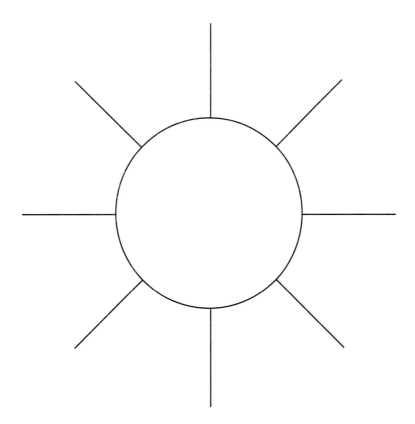

 What is the author's main message?

 What did you learn from the novel?

Name _____

Newspaper

Directions: Pretend you are a newspaper reporter interviewing Jay Berry about catching the escaped circus monkeys. Be sure to include a newspaper name, a headline for your article, and a picture to accompany your article.

Name _____

(Character Analysis)
A. Identification: Write two words to describe each character listed below.

1. Jay Berry: _____

2. Daisy: _____

3. Grandpa: _____

4. Rowdy: _____

(Main Idea and Details)
B. True/False: Mark each statement with a *T* for true or an *F* for false.

_____ 5. Jay Berry and Daisy are twins.

_____ 6. A problem at birth left one of Daisy's arms crippled.

_____ 7. Jay Berry's parents worked as sharecroppers before moving to Oklahoma.

_____ 8. The monkeys Jay Berry discovers escaped from a wrecked circus train.

_____ 9. Jay Berry plans to use the monkey reward money to buy a new work horse for the farm.

_____ 10. Jay Berry and his grandfather's first monkey-catching idea involves a butterfly net.

_____ 11. The monkeys steal Jay Berry's traps and gunny sack.

_____ 12. Jay Berry is afraid his hunting will offend the Old Man of the Mountains.

_____ 13. Jay Berry kills Gandy accidentally by trapping him in a net.

(Inferences)
C. Open-Ended Comprehension: Why do you think Jay Berry feels more confident after seeking advice from his grandfather and father?

_____

_____

_____

_____

_____

_____

_____

(Literary Devices)

A. Literary Devices: Identify each quote below as a simile (S) or metaphor (M). In the third column, explain what each simile or metaphor actually means.

Quote	S/M	Explanation
1. "I had taken [Rowdy] on several wasp-fighting expeditions and the little red warriors had really worked him over."		
2. "All at once the big monkey stopped squalling and the bottoms got as still as a graveyard."		
3. "Then up out of that green blanket and into the sky rose a flock of wild turkeys."		

(Sequencing)

B. Sequencing: Place the following events in the correct order using the letters *a–k*.

_____ 4. Jay Berry is impressed with the number of buildings, people, and wagons in Tahlequah.

_____ 5. Rowdy runs home ahead of the wagon.

_____ 6. Daisy nurses Jay Berry back to health after he drinks sour mash.

_____ 7. Daisy is angry that Jay Berry does not have her ribbon.

_____ 8. A girl at Wiley Mercantile tries to befriend Jay Berry.

_____ 9. Jay Berry and Rowdy each receive several bites from the little monkeys.

_____ 10. Grandpa and Jay Berry drink from "Jay Berry's Spring."

_____ 11. Rowdy disturbs an entire library.

_____ 12. Grandpa lets Jay Berry drive the wagon across the river to Tahlequah.

_____ 13. The monkeys steal coconuts out of the wagon.

_____ 14. Daisy suspects Jay Berry has hydrophobia.

A. Multiple Choice: Choose the BEST answer.

(Main Idea and Details)

_____ 1. Whom does Daisy see outside during the storm?
    a. Gandy
    b. Rowdy
    c. her mother and father
    d. the Old Man of the Mountains

(Drawing Conclusions)

_____ 2. Why doesn't Daisy want to tell her mother how much her leg hurts?
    a. She is afraid of visiting a doctor's office.
    b. She doesn't think her mother will believe her.
    c. She thinks her mother has enough to worry about.
    d. She knows the pain will eventually go away on its own.

(Main Idea and Details)

_____ 3. Daisy remembers the time Jay Berry got sick after he
    a. fell into the Lees' well
    b. drove a wagon across the river
    c. went hunting in the rain with Rowdy
    d. walked to Grandpa's store during a storm

(Main Idea and Details)

_____ 4. When Papa hears Daisy yell from the hillside, he assumes that Daisy has
    a. seen a snake
    b. lost her crutch
    c. found a fairy ring
    d. discovered a sick animal

(Inferences)

_____ 5. Why is the silence the Lees experience near Daisy's playhouse unusual?
    a. Mama would usually be praying to herself in such a situation.
    b. Daisy and Jay Berry would normally argue about taking turns.
    c. There are usually many sounds coming from the trees and animals.
    d. Rowdy normally would bark excitedly when the family was all together.

(Main Idea and Details)

_____ 6. To explain the legend of the fairy ring, Mama tells the story of
    a. herself and Papa
    b. her mother and father
    c. Johnnie George and Luann
    d. Teddy Roosevelt and his Rough Riders

(Point of View)

_____ 7. Papa thinks Daisy sees the Old Man of the Mountains because she is
      a. in extreme pain
      b. in tune with nature
      c. naïve and innocent
      d. the youngest in the family

(Setting)

_____ 8. Where does Jay Berry find the monkeys?
      a. hiding in the trees
      b. soaked in the river
      c. curled up under a washout
      d. crowded around the whiskey still

(Inferences)

_____ 9. The monkeys begin to trust Jay Berry because they
      a. are tired of obeying Jimbo
      b. realize he is only trying to help
      c. see how kind Jay Berry is to Rowdy
      d. know Jay Berry will take them to Daisy

(Cause/Effect)

_____ 10. What effect does seeing all of the monkeys have on Mama?
      a. She is angry.
      b. She is frightened.
      c. She feels grateful.
      d. She feels sorry for them.

(Conflict/Resolution)

B. Graphic Organizer: Describe how each conflict listed below is resolved in the novel.

Conflict	Resolution
11. Jay Berry cannot afford a pony and a gun.	
12. The Lees cannot afford surgery to straighten Daisy's leg.	
13. The Johnson brothers lose their trained monkeys.	

Name _____

(Literary Devices)
A. Literary Devices: Identify each quote below as a simile, a metaphor, or personification.

| a. simile | b. metaphor | c. personification |

_____ 1. "It started raining monkeys."

_____ 2. "The little devils stole everything I had...."

_____ 3. "...I was shaking like a corn tassel in a high wind."

_____ 4. "...[Rowdy's] tail...looked like a dead grapevine."

_____ 5. "...the beans...started crawling out of the pot...."

(Summarize Major Ideas)
B. Word Association: Explain how each of the following is important to the plot of *Summer of the Monkeys*.

6. Rowdy

_____

_____

_____

7. crutch

_____

_____

_____

8. Old Man of the Mountains

_____

_____

_____

9. fairy ring

_____

_____

_____

10. paint mare

_____

_____

_____

(Main Idea and Details)
C. True/False: Mark each with a *T* for true or an *F* for false.

_____ 11. Jay Berry is amazed when Jimbo figures out how to avoid the steel traps.

_____ 12. Daisy believes the Old Man of the Mountains protects young children.

_____ 13. Jay Berry's fairy ring wish is for a pony and a .22.

_____ 14. The monkeys eventually go willingly with Jay Berry because they are drunk.

_____ 15. Grandpa chooses the paint mare for a specific reason.

_____ 16. Jimbo is reluctant to leave with the Johnson brothers.

_____ 17. Daisy and Mama bring Jay Berry the gun he has always wanted.

_____ 18. Jay Berry names the paint mare Dolly.

(Cause/Effect)
D. Graphic Organizer: List a cause for each effect in the chart below.

Cause	Effect
19.	Jay Berry tries to catch the monkeys with a net.
20.	Rowdy wants nothing to do with the monkeys.
21.	Jay Berry comes home drunk.
22.	Jay Berry travels with Grandpa to town.
23.	Grandpa gets angry at the monkeys.
24.	Daisy has surgery on her leg.

© Novel Units, Inc.

E. Essay: On a separate sheet of paper, write a two- to three-paragraph response for two of the following.

(Interpret Text)
   a. Why does Papa tell Jay Berry he "grew ten feet tall" (p. 270) on the day he gives his reward money to Mama?

(Character Analysis)
   b. How does Jay Berry's relationship with the monkeys change from the beginning to the end of the novel?

(Setting)
   c. How does the novel's setting affect the story? How might the story have been different if set in a different time and place?

(Point of View)
   d. How might the story have been different if written from Daisy's point of view?

(Theme)
   e. Explain how one of the following themes is interlaced throughout the novel: faith, sacrifice, determination.

Answer Key

Activity #1: Answers will vary.

Activity #2: Title of Novel: *Summer of the Monkeys*; Predictions and illustrations will vary.

Activity #3: 1. sharecropper 2. grove 3. contraption 4. slough 5. liable 6. lobe 7. radiant 8. peddler 9. jarred 10.–11. Definitions for "altar" and "scalded" will vary.

Activity #4: Nouns—kindling, briers, timber; Verbs—squalling, loping, hallowed, darted; Adjectives—quavering, spindly, superstitious; Adverbs—none

Activity #5: **A.** 1. e 2. i 3. g 4. b 5. d 6. f 7. a 8. h 9. c **B.** Summaries will vary.

Activity #6: Word maps will vary. Example—Vocabulary Word: unruly; Definition: difficult to control or manage; Synonym: wild; Antonym: well-behaved; Pronunciation: un-ROO-lee; Part of Speech: adjective; Sentence: The *unruly* crowd pressed even closer to the concert stage.

Activity #7: Mobiles will vary. Example—Vocabulary Word: pitiful; Definition: deserving pity or compassion; Synonym: pathetic; Antonym: admirable; Sentence: My younger brother looked *pitiful* as he gazed longingly into the store window at the newest gaming system; Pictures will vary.

Activity #8:

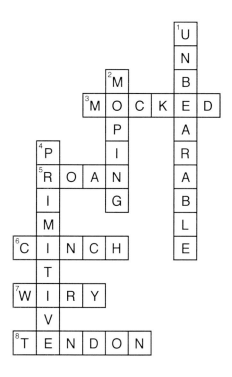

Study Guide

Chapters 1–3: 1. in the foothills of the Ozark Mountains in the middle of the Cherokee Nation 2. Jay Berry was born completely healthy, but Daisy was born with a crippled leg. 3. Jay Berry's grandfather traded with some Cherokee Indians for it and then offered it to his daughter and son-in-law. 4. The family had waited so long for land of their own that she was determined to reach the land as soon as possible. 5. with corn-shuck dolls, mud pies, pretty bottles, tin cans filled with flowers, and an altar 6. Rowdy protects Jay Berry and can easily sniff out Sally Gooden, the Lees' dairy cow. 7. Papa believes the monkey was a wealthy family's escaped pet. 8. He thinks the monkey, along with many other monkeys, escaped from a wrecked circus train. 9. He wraps small steel traps with strips of cloth so the traps won't harm the monkeys. Then he advises Jay Berry to bait the traps with apples. 10. a pony and a .22 11. Daisy thinks Jay Berry plans on killing the monkeys. 12. the Old Man of the Mountains

Chapters 4–6: 1. Papa thinks Jay Berry may be underestimating the monkeys' intelligence. He doesn't want Jay Berry to be disappointed if he can't catch the monkeys. 2. He fears the Old Man of the Mountains will curse him with bad luck if he or Rowdy hurts any small animals. 3. a small boy 4. The first time, the hundred dollar monkey simply pulls the apples off the nails. The second time, the monkey uses a stick to spring each trap so he can steal the apples. 5. The monkeys steal everything. 6. He throws a chunk of dirt and shoots several rocks at the monkey. 7. The hundred dollar monkey is their leader and warns them of danger, keeping them from being caught. 8. His clothes are torn from running through the brush. 9. a special net with pull strings that open and close it 10. Jay Berry describes her as "one of the best little old grandmas a boy ever had" (p. 81). She worries about Jay Berry's health and schooling and is constantly feeding him when he comes to her house. 11. for an operation that will fix Daisy's leg 12. Gandy, a mean old goose on the Lees' farm 13. Papa

Chapters 7–9: 1. a snake and a hornet 2. One monkey bites Jay Berry because he startles the monkey by touching him. The other monkey bites Rowdy after Rowdy shakes it in defense of Jay Berry. 3. to free the two small monkeys in the net 4. All of the other small monkeys attack them. Jay Berry and Rowdy are drastically outnumbered, so they flee. 5. hydrophobia 6. She transports Rowdy in a wheelbarrow. 7. three days 8. Jimbo; He wrote a letter to the circus trainer who trained Jimbo and the other monkeys. 9. He advises Jay Berry to befriend them. 10. drinking from an old whiskey still in the river bottoms 11. Jimbo is insulted by the refusal of the gift. 12. his pants 13. She is upset both that Jay Berry is drunk and that she thinks he may be lying to her about what happened.

Chapters 10–12: 1. that it will get a person just as drunk and twice as sick as alcohol because it sits in the stomach and ferments 2. She loves going with her parents to her grandparents' store. 3. so he will throw up and rid his stomach of the fermenting sour mash 4. He believes one can find the answer to any problem in a library. 5. He offers to let Jay Berry drive the wagon and team across a river. 6. It is a large, red-brick building with stone steps and marble columns, surrounded by a green lawn and large trees. 7. *Trapping Monkeys in the Jungles of Borneo* 8. to buy some coconuts 9. He buys pink and blue ribbon for Daisy, a thimble for his mother, and a shaving mug for his father. 10. He plans to catch the monkeys in a pen built from chicken wire, using the coconuts as bait. 11. While Jay Berry and his grandfather are drinking from a nearby spring, the monkeys steal things from their wagon. 12. He promises her Sally Gooden's next calf.

Chapters 13–15: 1. He is afraid the monkeys will drown. 2. that it has been hurting more than usual lately and pains her particularly badly during storms 3. standing outside, smiling and pointing a stick at the Lees' house 4. work in the blacksmith shop 5. She discovers a fairy ring—a perfectly spaced circle of white toadstools. 6. Luann and Johnnie George 7. that Daisy's leg will get fixed 8. Jay Berry hears whimpering and follows the sound to the washout. 9. Jay Berry is able to handle the monkeys without being bitten or scratched, most likely because they realize he is now trying to help them. 10. He carries them to a sunny spot and helps dry them off. 11. because the monkeys, living most of their lives in captivity, were so frightened by the storm that they decided to let themselves be caught 12. Mama offers to get them some warm milk, Daisy offers to get them some apples, and Papa offers to make them a straw bed.

Chapters 16–19: 1. At first, they plan to send a letter, but then the mailman offers to send a telegram for them. 2. He gets a giant bone. 3. to pick up ponies for Jay Berry to choose from 4. He leaps into his arms and whimpers. 5. $156 6. The paint pony is beautiful, looks like she can run fast, isn't skittish, gets along with Rowdy, seems to have a connection with Jay Berry, and is exactly the kind of pony Jay Berry dreamed of owning. However, he is hesitant to choose her because her leg is injured. 7. Answers will vary, but Jay Berry is most likely both disappointed that he will not get his pony after all and disappointed that he didn't understand his grandfather's hints about what Jay Berry should do with the money. 8. First, they all become quiet, then Mama and Daisy begin to cry. Finally, everyone is excited about what the money means for Daisy. 9. They can hardly cook for themselves and soon become anxious and sad. 10. Her crippled leg has been operated on and is indistinguishable from her other "good" leg. 11. the paint mare 12. run with her

Note: Answers to Activities #9–#21 will vary. Suggested responses are given where applicable.

Activity #9: Suggestions—1. Jay Berry attempts to trap the monkeys using wrapped traps and apples. 2. Jay Berry catches two small monkeys in his net. 3. Jay Berry tries to befriend the monkeys at the whiskey still. 4. Jay Berry finds the frightened monkeys in the washout after a big storm. Descriptions/illustrations will vary.

Activity #10: Example—Character: Jay Berry; What Character Does: performs farm chores, hunts, explores, traps monkeys; Why He Does It: He is a curious country boy who learns there is reward money being offered for the escaped monkeys; Significant About Name: Jay Berry's name reflects his rural upbringing; Nature of Actions: Jay Berry is reactive, often responding impulsively or foolishly in situations; Significance of Time and Place: The novel's time (late 1800s) is important because it sets the scene for Jay Berry's escapades on a small, recently settled farm in the river bottoms of the Ozark Mountains. Time and place also tie in significantly with Jay Berry's monkey-trapping solutions. Unusual/Important About Character: Jay Berry is a nature-loving, mischief-seeking boy, but he is also compassionate and cares fiercely for his family; How Character Changes: Jay Berry transitions from "me-centered" behavior at the beginning of the story to noble, selfless behavior at the end of the story; Answers will vary.

Activity #11: Suggestions—Character: Jay Berry; Conflict: Jay Berry wants to catch the monkeys and collect the reward money, but the monkeys thwart him at every turn; Resolution: The monkeys come with Jay Berry willingly after a large, violent storm frightens them; Character: Daisy; Conflict: Daisy suffers tremendous pain in her crippled leg, but her family does not have the money for the operation to fix it; Resolution: Jay Berry donates his reward money toward Daisy's surgery, and together with the family's meager savings, the money is enough to pay for Daisy's operation; Characters: the Johnson brothers; Conflict: The brothers' circus train wrecks, and their trained monkeys vanish into the woods; Resolution: Motivated by the reward money, Jay Berry finally captures the monkeys and returns them to the Johnson brothers.

Activity #12: Suggestions—Jay Berry: honest, naïve, passionate, curious; Grandpa: smart, funny, wise, generous; Daisy: compassionate, kind, strong-willed, patient; Papa: hardworking, calm, logical, resolute; Mama: protective, loving, faithful, hopeful; Jay Berry to Grandpa: admiring; Grandpa to Jay Berry: guiding; Jay Berry to Daisy: caring; Daisy to Jay Berry: concerned; Jay Berry to Papa: respectful; Papa to Jay Berry: proud; Jay Berry to Mama: loving; Mama to Jay Berry: worried

Activity #13: Suggestions—The Johnson brothers arrive at the Lee farm, and Jimbo is reunited with his owners; Grandpa brings two horses to his store for Jay Berry to choose between, and Jay Berry has a realization after choosing the injured paint mare; Jay Berry gives his mother his reward money, and Daisy can have the surgery to repair her leg.

Activity #14: Example—Jay Berry's World: Jay Berry rarely sees automobiles; My World: Most people in today's world see numerous automobiles on a regular basis.

Activity #15: Example—Problem: Jay Berry is unable to catch the monkeys using traps; Character's Solution: Jay Berry attempts to catch the monkeys using a net; Your Solution: Answers will vary.

Activity #16: Suggestions—Daisy is frightened and flees to Jay Berry's room, Daisy confesses that her leg pains her more than anyone knows, Jay Berry feels sorry for his sister; The monkeys are frightened and hide in a washout, Jay Berry leads the monkeys to the Lees' farm, Jay Berry collects the reward money from the Johnson brothers.

Activity #17: Riddles will vary.

Activity #18: Setting: the Ozark Mountains in the late 1800s; Characters: Jay Berry, Daisy, Mama, Papa, Grandpa, Rowdy, the monkeys; Problem: Jay Berry Lee wants to catch some escaped circus monkeys so he can afford the pony and gun he always wanted; Conflict: The monkeys steal Jay Berry's traps and bait; Conflict: The monkeys attack Rowdy and Jay Berry severely on one occasion; Conflict: The monkeys get Jay Berry drunk and steal his pants on another occasion; Climax: A huge storm hits the area, making the monkeys more vulnerable to being caught; Turning Point Incident: The monkeys willingly accompany Jay Berry to the Lee farm and are reunited with Ben and Tom Johnson; Resolution: Jay Berry uses his reward money to help pay for Daisy's surgery rather than spending it on himself.

Activity #19: Answers will vary.

Activity #20: Example—Theme: hope; At first, Papa and Mama are sharecroppers, but they constantly hope that one day they will have their own farm; Papa and Mama acquire land through Grandpa and hope that their little farm can survive; Papa and Mama have Jay Berry and Daisy and hope that they can afford an operation to straighten Daisy's leg; Jay Berry discovers the monkeys in the river bottoms and hopes he can catch them; Jay Berry and Grandpa design monkey traps and hope they will work; Jay Berry and

36 | © Novel Units, Inc.

Grandpa visit the library, hoping to find some information on monkey-trapping; Daisy finds a fairy ring, and the Lees hope that their wishes come true; Jay Berry finally catches the monkeys and hopes his dream of owning a pony and a gun will finally come true; Answers will vary.

Activity #21: Articles will vary.

Quiz #1: A. Answers will vary. Suggestions—1. determined, honest 2. thoughtful, compassionate 3. adventurous, knowledgeable 4. loyal, comical **B.** 5. T 6. F 7. T 8. T 9. F 10. F 11. T 12. T 13. F **C.** Answers will vary but should include that Jay Berry's grandfather and father are the major male influences in his life. Jay Berry values their advice because he admires them and trusts their wisdom gained through experience.

Quiz #2: A. 1. M (p. 102); Explanation—Rowdy had been stung repeatedly by wasps in the past. 2. S (p. 107); Explanation—The river bottoms were so still you couldn't hear anything moving or breathing. 3. M (p. 154); The grass was so smooth and uniform it appeared to be a green blanket. **B.** 4. e 5. j 6. c 7. k 8. g 9. a 10. h 11. f 12. d 13. i 14. b

Quiz #3: A. 1. d 2. c 3. a 4. a 5. c 6. c 7. a 8. c 9. b 10. b **B.** Answers will vary. Suggestions—11. Jay Berry's family gets him the pony, and Daisy and his mother buy him a gun. 12. Jay Berry uses his reward money to pay for Daisy's surgery. 13. Jay Berry captures the monkeys and returns them to the Johnson brothers.

Novel Test: A. 1. b (p. 47) 2. b (p. 63) 3. a (p. 133) 4. a (p. 159) 5. c (p. 272) **B.** Answers will vary. Suggestions—6. Rowdy is Jay Berry's constant companion throughout the novel. The two are inseparable, and Rowdy even travels into town with Jay Berry and his grandfather. Rowdy is also Jay Berry's fiercest defender. Whatever trouble Jay Berry encounters, Rowdy is by his side. Rowdy also provides comic relief in the novel. 7. Daisy's father made the crutch for her when she became unable to put weight on her leg. The crutch is imperative for Daisy's mobility, as it allows her to move around more easily. At the end of the story, Mama insists on keeping Daisy's crutch so the family will always be grateful for their blessings. 8. The Old Man of the Mountains is a figure only Daisy sees. She believes the old man is a caretaker of nature and can grant good or bad luck to people. Papa theorizes that Daisy may be seeing the spirit of Christ. 9. Daisy discovers a fairy ring, or circle of white toadstools spaced perfectly apart. According to legend, wishes made in the center of a fairy ring will come true. Indeed, each wish Jay Berry's family members make from within the fairy ring has come true by the novel's end. 10. The paint mare is the pony Jay Berry has always dreamed about owning, and the two seem to share a special connection. The mare's injured leg prompts an important realization for Jay Berry—that he should use his reward money for Daisy's surgery. **C.** 11. T 12. F 13. F 14. F 15. T 16. F 17. T 18. T **D.** Answers will vary. Suggestions—19. Jay Berry fails to capture the monkeys using traps. 20. The monkeys attack Rowdy, leaving him tired and ill for days. 21. Jay Berry tries to befriend the monkeys at the whiskey still and, to make Jimbo happy, he drinks sour mash from the still. 22. Grandpa decides that he and Jay Berry need to research techniques for monkey-catching. 23. The monkeys steal coconuts from the wagon and seem to be laughing at Grandpa and Jay Berry. 24. Jay Berry decides against the pony and .22 he has wanted for so long and instead donates his reward money toward Daisy's surgery. **E.** Essays will vary. Refer to the scoring rubric on page 38 of this guide.

Linking Novel Units® Student Packets to National and State Reading Assessments

During the past several years, an increasing number of students have faced some form of state-mandated competency testing in reading. Many states now administer state-developed assessments to measure the skills and knowledge emphasized in their particular reading curriculum. This Novel Units® guide includes open-ended comprehension questions that correlate with state-mandated reading assessments. The rubric below provides important information for evaluating responses to open-ended comprehension questions. Teachers may also use scoring rubrics provided for their own state's competency test.

Scoring Rubric for Open-Ended Items

3-Exemplary
Thorough, complete ideas/information
Clear organization throughout
Logical reasoning/conclusions
Thorough understanding of reading task
Accurate, complete response

2-Sufficient
Many relevant ideas/pieces of information
Clear organization throughout most of response
Minor problems in logical reasoning/conclusions
General understanding of reading task
Generally accurate and complete response

1-Partially Sufficient
Minimally relevant ideas/information
Obvious gaps in organization
Obvious problems in logical reasoning/conclusions
Minimal understanding of reading task
Inaccuracies/incomplete response

0-Insufficient
Irrelevant ideas/information
No coherent organization
Major problems in logical reasoning/conclusions
Little or no understanding of reading task
Generally inaccurate/incomplete response

Notes

Notes